Bingo was a small black and white
puppy.
He had two bright eyes, a big wet
nose and a very waggly tail.
One day Bingo woke up feeling
very hungry.

'I can eat a sausage,'
said Bingo.

'Yum, yum!' said Bingo.

'I can eat crisps,'
said Bingo.

'Yum, yum!' said Bingo.

'I can see a jelly,'
said Bingo.

'I want to eat it.'

'Help!' said Bingo.